This series concentrates upon the basics of the English Language.

The activities are straightforward, brief and to the point. They offer repetition and progression providing a firm grounding in the language.

Each book covers: Writing
Spelling
Grammar
Comprehension

New Treasury of English 1

New Treasury of English is a core scheme that aims to introduce children to the salient features of English grammar. The series develops their ability to comprehend written passages and utilises both grammar and comprehension in a series of relevant and structured exercises. The passages have been carefully chosen to give a wide variety of interesting material drawn from both fact and fiction.

How the books are constructed
Comprehension: The passages are of varying length and complexity. The child is asked a series of questions. In some cases the answers are explicit in the passages while in others they are implicit. Some questions go beyond the confines of the passage and draw on the pupil's general experience and skills. In addition, there are a number of exercises designed to encourage children to look for meaning in writing rather than to merely decode words.

Grammar: The only grammar introduced is that which will enhance the child's style of writing and speech. Grammar is not treated as an end in itself: technical names for parts of speech are not used at this level. Each point is introduced by a brief explanation and followed by several sets of reinforcement and consolidation exercises.

Written style: In each book there are several sections that aim to broaden and develop pupil's written style. These vary from highlighting over-used words and suggesting alternatives to extending sentence construction.

How to use these books
Each book contains more work than is likely to be needed in one school year. You will probably need to be selective by either concentrating on one particular aspect of the book, say grammar or style, or by deciding that it is not necessary for the pupils to complete every exercise. The comprehension passages in particular lend themselves to a variety of approaches. They can be used by the individual child as well as by the group, thus providing the basis for useful discussion. They could also be used as oral exercises. By starting with some of the shorter passages you could provide a progressive course in listening skills.

Whatever you decide to do, you will find that *New Treasury of English* provides a core scheme and will enable the teacher to achieve a high degree of flexibility of approach.

© 1995 Folens Publishers Ltd, Dunstable and Dublin.
Folens Ltd, Albert House, Apex Business Centre, Boscombe Road, Dunstable, LU5 4RL, United Kingdom.

ISBN 185276 017-6   Printed in Singapore by Craft Print.

CONTENTS

Who am I?

My name is _____ .
I am _____ years old.
I have _____ eyes.
I have _____ hair.

I live at _____ .
There are _____ people in my family.

I go to school in _____ .
My school is in _____ .
I am in _____ class.
My teacher's name is _____ .
There are _____ children in my class.

Autumn

The months of autumn are August, September and October.

In autumn we have less sunshine. Some days can be very windy and wet.

Many trees, like the horse-chestnut, the beech and the oak lose their leaves. The leaves turn yellow, red, brown and gold.

The swallow and the cuckoo leave Britain for warmer countries. They will return in the spring.

The squirrel and the hedgehog get their homes ready for a long winter sleep.

The apples, pears and plums are ripe in the orchards. They are ready for picking.

In autumn the farmer is very busy clearing the fields and getting the land ready to plant next year's crops.

Question Time

1. How many months are there in autumn?
2. Name the months of autumn.
3. What kind of weather can we have in autumn?
4. What happens to many trees in autumn?
5. What birds leave Britain in autumn?
6. Why do some birds leave Britain at that time?
7. Name one animal that sleeps a lot in winter.
8. Name two fruits that ripen in autumn.
9. Apple trees grow in an _____ .
10. What work does the farmer do in autumn?

Fire! Fire!

Brian was  down the  .

Suddenly he saw  pouring out of an old

 .  he

Brian  to the nearest  .

He  999 for the  .

Soon the  came. They rolled out the .

Quickly they poured  over the  .

The  put out the  in ten minutes.

Question Time

1. Who was out walking?
2. What did Brian see?
3. Where was the smoke coming from?
4. Where did Brian run for help?
5. How did Brian get the fire-brigade?
6. What did the firemen roll out?
7. What was used to put out the fire?
8. Was the fire put out quickly?

Choose the correct word.

1. Brian was out (climbing, swimming, walking).
2. Brian saw (food, water, smoke).
3. The house on fire was (new, old, bright).
4. Brian shouted (help, fire, hello).
5. Brian ran to the nearest (school, house, church).
6. Brian rang (the police, the fire-brigade, home).
7. The firemen rolled out (carpet, hoses, paper).
8. The fire was put out with (milk, sand, water).

Autumn

Trace and colour the pictures. Finish off the words.

Autumn can be w_t and windy.

Squirrels gather n_ts in autumn.

Birds get ready for winter.

Some trees los_ their leaves.

Autumn is a good time for fruit.

Farmers plough the fi_lds.

Grammar

We use capital letters at the start of all sentences.

A.   Write these sentences correctly.

1.   here comes the bus.
2.   it is a very sunny day.
3.   we love ice-cream and sweets.
4.   the children are playing in the yard.
5.   when is the next train going?
6.   school starts at nine o'clock.
7.   one day I got lost in the park.
8.   your bag is in the kitchen.

A, E, I, O, U, are called vowels.
Before a word beginning with **a** or **e** or **i** or **o** or **u** you must always use **an** instead of **a**.

We say, **an e**lephant, **an a**pple, **an i**ndian, **an o**range, **an u**mbrella.

B.   Put *a* or *an* in the space.

1.   Ann was reading ___ book.
2.   My daddy ate ___ egg.
3.   ___ elephant is a very big animal.
4.   I fell off ___ chair.
5.   ___ apple a day keeps the doctor away.
6.   I need ___ umbrella for the rain.

The Red Squirrel

The red squirrel has a soft fur. It is light brown, almost red. The squirrel's tail is as long as its body. It keeps it warm and helps it jump from tree to tree.

The squirrel's home is called a drey. It makes it near the top of a tall tree. It is made of twigs, moss and leaves.

The baby squirrels are born in spring. In autumn the squirrel gathers nuts and hides them in many places. Sometimes it forgets where it hides the nuts. The squirrel holds an acorn in its front paws and eats it with its sharp teeth.

The squirrel sleeps for most of the winter but sometimes wakes to eat.

Question Time.

1. What colour is the red squirrel's fur?
2. How long is the squirrel's tail?
3. Why does the squirrel have a long tail?
4. What is the squirrel's home called?
5. Where does the squirrel make its nest?
6. What does the squirrel use to make its nest?
7. When are baby squirrels born?
8. What food does the squirrel eat?
9. What does the squirrel do in autumn?
10. Does the squirrel sleep all winter?

How many can you find?   Wordsearch

Squirrel
Moss
Twig
Leaves
Acorn
Drey
Tail
Brown
Paw
Autumn
Tree
Nut

S	N	L	E	A	V	E	S
A	Q	U	P	A	W	T	■
A	S	U	T	C	I	A	M
U	T	Q	I	O	G	I	H
T	R	U	U	R	H	L	S
U	E	O	Y	N	R	Y	S
M	E	E	W	D	R	E	Y
N	B	R	O	W	N	J	L

Phonics - short vowels *a, e, i, o, u*

A. Write the *vowel* sound the word begins with.

_____   _____   _____

_____   _____   _____

B. Look at the picture. Then read the three words beside it. Write out the correct word.

tip top tap	bad bed bid	tip tap top
pin pen pan	bun bin ban	ton tin ten
log lag leg	cap cup cop	pig peg pug

Phonics — short vowels *a, e, i, o, u*

A. Look at the picture. Listen carefully for the sound in the middle, write the word on a piece of paper.

hat   _ _ _   _ _ _

_ _ _   _ _ _   _ _ _

_ _ _   _ _ _   _ _ _

B. Re-write the sentences putting in the words for the pictures.

1. The  eats the

2. The likes the

3. The is in

13

The Foolish Crow

One day, a crow was flying to her nest. She saw some cheese on a bird-table.

The bird flew down. She sat on the roof of a house. She waited until no one was around.

Then, she flew to the bird-table and took the cheese. She went to a tree where she was going to eat it.

A hungry fox saw the crow. He wanted the cheese. Suddenly, the animal had a clever idea.

"Hello, Mrs. Crow," he said. "You do look pretty!" The crow was so pleased, but, said nothing. She just nodded her head.

"Oh, Mrs. Crow," you must be a lovely singer!" The bird was so pleased that she tried to sing. The cheese fell. The fox snapped it up and ran off with it.

Question Time.

1. Who was flying to her nest?
2. What did the crow see?
3. Where did the crow see the cheese?
4. Where did the crow wait?
5. Where did the crow fly with the cheese?
6. What animal saw the crow?
7. What did the crow do when the fox told her that she was pretty?
8. What did the fox tell the crow next?
9. What did the crow do when she heard that she was a lovely singer?
10. What did the fox do when the cheese fell?

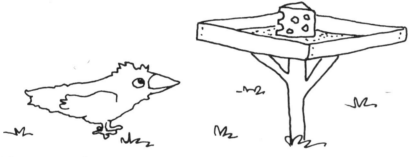

Choose the correct word.

1. The crow was flying to her (den, house, nest).
2. The crow saw some (bread, cheese, milk).
3. The crow saw the cheese on a (roof, tree, bird-table).
4. The crow flew to a (tree, nest, table) to eat.
5. A (dog, wolf, fox) saw the crow.
6. The fox told the crow that she was (ugly, bad, pretty).
7. The crow was (sad, pleased, mad).
8. The fox (ate, snapped up, left) the cheese.
9. The crow was a (clever, wise, foolish) bird.
10. The fox was a (stupid, clever, silly) animal.

Grammar

We use capital letters at the start of all sentences and a full stop at the end.

A.   Write these sentences correctly.

1.   next Wednesday I am going swimming
2.   the boy ran across the road
3.   my name is John
4.   his mother is in hospital
5.   the house was burnt down
6.   we will meet at the cinema
7.   he eats too many chocolates
8.   they are not doing their work

B.   Put *I* or *me* in the following sentences.

1.   ___ want to look at the television.
2.   He asked ___ about the picture.
3.   ___ fell off my bike.
4.   Do you want ___ to go?
5.   My mother gave it to ___ .
6.   ___ am waiting for the bus.
7.   She pushed ___ into the water.
8.   In the garden ___ saw a bird.

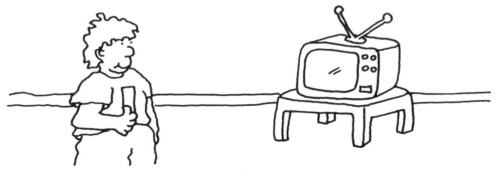

Exercises

A. **The words in these sentences are mixed up. Write them correctly.**

1. going Ann to school is
2. children are the running quickly
3. teacher cross very is the
4. have apple I an lunch my for
5. live small a house I in
6. sunny it a day is
7. read we can story a
8. seven there days in a week are

---

to too two

Examples: – I have **two** sweets.
It is **too** cold for ice-cream.
I have **to** get a new copy.
Pat went home and Ann went **too.**

B. **Put** *to, too, two* **in the space.**

1. I have ___ hands and ___ feet.
2. It is ___ hot to run.
3. I have ___ go ___ the shop.
4. Ann is sick and Mary is ___ .
5. Please may I have ___ apples?
6. The boy is ___ small for school.
7. I am going to swimming ___ .
8. We want ___ eat and ___ drink.

The Hedgehog

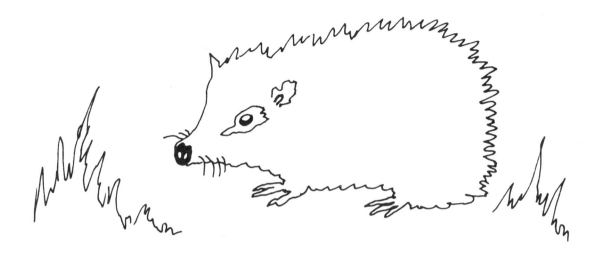

The hedgehog has sharp bristles all over his back. They are brown with pale tips. His legs are very short. He has bright eyes and a blunt nose.

His home is a hole in a ditch. It is made of leaves, moss and dry grass.

Baby hedgehogs are born in the summer. For the first four weeks their coats are soft.

The hedgehog hunts at night. If a fox or a person comes close to him he rolls himself into a ball. His bristles stick out all over him and no one can touch him.

The hedgehog is a good animal to have in a garden. He eats all the snails, slugs and other pests.

Sadly, many hedgehogs are killed by cars when crossing the road.

The hedgehog does not store food for the winter but he does sleep on a bed of dry leaves until spring. This is called **hibernation.**

Question Time.

1. What is a hedgehog's coat like?
2. What kind of legs has a hedgehog got?
3. Where does the hedgehog make his home?
4. What does the hedgehog use to make its home?
5. When are baby hedgehogs born?
6. What kind of coat do baby hedgehogs have?
7. When does the hedgehog hunt?
8. What does the hedgehog do when he meets an enemy?
9. Why should a gardener like the hedgehog?
10. What does the hedgehog do in winter?

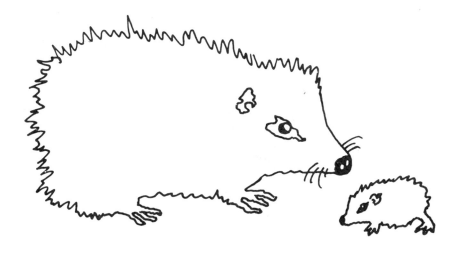

Write these words correctly. You will find them on page 18.

rbisltes	_____	erhibantino	_____
olhe	_____	sotre	_____
nasil	_____	ossm	_____
utaumn	_____	unths	_____

Phonics - long *a* with magic *e*.

Say the *a* sound.
It is a short sound.

Say the *a* sound.
It is a long sound.
The magic **e** at the end.
turns the *a* into the name of the letter.

A. **Write the missing *a* and magic *e*.**
Then, *read* the word.

l _ c _	r _ k _	t _ p _

B. **Write the missing letters.**
***Remember* the magic e.**
Then *read* the word.

ca _ _	ca _ _	fa _ _
ga _ _	ıa _ _	ha _ _

A. Write the missing letters. Read the sentence.

1. I c _ m _ home at ten o'clock.
2. Mummy can b _ k _ lovely buns.
3. My birthday c _ k _ is finished.
4. The l_n_ goes to the farm.
5. I am never l _ t _ for school.
6. I w _ k _ up early.
7. The dog has a l _ m _ leg.
8. I h _ t _ getting up early.

B. Read each sentence carefully. Choose the correct word.

1. I (at, ate) my lunch.
2. I have a new (hate, hat).
3. I wipe my feet on the (mat, mate).
4. I (hat, hate) the rain.
5. A horse has a (mane, man).
6. The tree looks very (bar, bare).
7. Both of those pictures are the (sam, same).
8. Teacher is very (made, mad) with me.

Exercises

**A. These sentences are not in the correct order.
Write them in the correct order.**

1. I opened the door.
    I got up out of my chair.
    I heard a knock on the door.

2. I get out of bed.
    I wash myself.
    I wake up.

3. I go to the shop.
    I get ten pence.
    I buy crisps.

---

of   off

Examples: – I had two cups **of** tea.
I fell **off** my bicycle.

B. Put *of* or *off* in the space.

1. I am afraid _____ the dark.
2. The match is _____ as it is raining.
3. I need a lot _____ money.
4. Get _____ that wall!
5. Six _____ the children are sick.
6. I would like six _____ those pears.
7. I was knocked _____ the chair.
8. Please let me _____ at twelve o'clock.

Winter

The months of winter are November, December and January.

In winter the weather is very cold. There is frost and snow. We wear warm woolly clothes. We need heat in the house.

Most trees are bare except for the evergreens, like holly. The holly tree has a lovely red berry. No flowers or grass grow.

Many creatures are asleep, such as the squirrel, the hedgehog, the ladybird and the snail.

If it snows heavily the farmer may not be able to get to his animals with food. Sometimes food is air-dropped for them by helicopter.

Huge flocks of geese leave their very cold homes in Greenland and come to Britain for the winter.

When the ground is frozen birds cannot find food or water. We must remember to put out food for them.

Question Time.
1. What are the months of winter?
2. How many months are there in winter?
3. What kind of weather do we have in winter?
4. How is your house heated?
5. Name one evergreen tree.
6. Why is food sometimes air-dropped?
7. What animals is the food air-dropped for?
8. Why do some geese come to Britain for winter?
9. What food can you put out for the birds?
10. What clothes do you wear in winter?

Trace and colour the pictures. Finish off the words.

We need to keep w_rm.

Many trees have be___ies.

Some animals s__ep all winter.

Farmers drop h__ to the sheep.

Geese spend winter in Br_tain.

We can put out f___d for birds.

Puzzle time 1

Can you find a little word in each of these?

1	stand		6	spend	
2	fill		7	cork	
3	spot		8	that	
4	mats		9	stop	
5	thin		10	this	

Can you find 12 words in this puzzle?
Read across and down.

Write out the 12 words on the lines.

1. . . . .   2. . . . .   3. . . . .   4. . . . .
5. . . . .   6. . . . .   7. . . . .   8. . . . .
9. . . . .   10. . . . .   11. . . . .   12. . . . .

What am I?

1. I have a tail but no legs. I swim in the sea. _____

2. I have just come out of an egg. _____

3. You walk with us. _____

Bright Eyes

Hello everybody. My name is Bright Eyes. I have four legs. I have a brown fur with white patches. My tail is very short but my two ears are very long. Guess what I am? Yes! I am a rabbit.

I was born in a pet shop. When I was about two months old I was bought by the O'Neill family. My home is the back garden where I can run and play all day long.

One day, I made Mr. and Mrs. O'Neill very cross. I got into the vegetable garden. I had a great feast of carrots and lettuce. I ate so much I nearly got sick.

The O'Neill children love to show me to their friends. I have one enemy. That is the dog next door. I think that he would like to have me for his tea.

I am very excited because next week the O'Neills are getting another rabbit to keep me company.

A. Question Time

1. What does Bright Eyes look like?
2. What is Bright Eyes?
3. Where was Bright Eyes born?
4. Who does Bright Eyes live with?
5. Where is Bright Eyes' home?
6. Where did Bright Eyes go one day?
7. How did Mr. and Mrs. O'Neill feel?
8. What does Bright Eyes like to eat?
9. Who is Bright Eyes' enemy?
10. Why is Bright Eyes excited?

B. Choose the correct word.

1. Bright Eyes is a (horse, rabbit, squirrel).
2. Bright Eyes has (two, four, six) legs.
3. Bright Eyes has (dull, red, bright) eyes.
4. Bright Eyes was born in a (stable, burrow, pet shop).
5. Bright Eyes was (stolen, bought, found).
6. Mr. and Mrs. O'Neill were (cross, sad, happy).
7. Bright Eyes ate (sweets, fruit, vegetables).
8. Bright Eyes' enemy is a (fox, cat, dog).
9. Bright Eyes lives in a (garden, shop, house).
10. Bright Eyes is (mad, unhappy, excited) because another rabbit is coming.

Grammar

The names of people always begin with a *capital letter.*

A. Write these sentences correctly.

1. ann lives in Bradford.
2. tom and jerry make me laugh.
3. peter is a good singer.
4. barry drives a big lorry.
5. dan is a very fat man.
6. john is at the cinema.
7. mary eats ice-cream.
8. frank can draw lovely pictures.

We use *is* when we are speaking about *one* thing.
We use *are* when we are speaking about *more than one* thing.

B. Put *is* or *are* in the spaces.

1. The egg ___ in the nest.
2. The birds ___ in the nest.
3. This ___ my brother.
4. Some of the children ___ here.
5. There ___ my new raincoat.
6. ___ they all going out?
7. He ___ very sorry.
8. We ___ going to the shop.

Exercises

We often see the two together.
Choose the correct word from the words given
below. Write it in your book.

salt	milk	saucer	fork	bat
butter	thread	comb	key	pencil

1. bread and _____
2. pepper and _____
3. knife and _____
4. pen and _____
5. cup and _____

6. sugar and _____
7. ball and _____
8. needle and _____
9. brush and _____
10. lock and _____

hear   here.
Examples: I **hear** the bird singing.
I live **here.**
I **hear** with my ears.
Please come over **here.**

Put *here* **or** *hear* **in the space.**
1. Did you _____ the wind last night?
2. John lives _____ in Cardiff.
3. Mummy, the book isn't _____ .
4. We _____ the music playing.
5. _____ is my lost shoe!
6. I cannot _____ what you are saying.
7. _____ comes Pat the Postman.

Robin Redbreast

The robin is a small bird. Cock Robin – that is, the father Robin – has a bright red breast, brown wings and a plump body.

The robin is the tamest of all our garden birds. He is a very sweet singer.

In spring, Cock Robin finds a Hen Robin – that is the mother Robin. They build a nest. The Hen Robin lays 3 to 7 white-coloured eggs.

The young birds are naked. It takes them 2 to 3 weeks to grow feathers. Their parents teach them how to sing, fly and find food. Robins eat snails and worms.

Many young robins die before they are a year old. Cats, rats and owls kill some, but the cold is their worst enemy. Snow, frost and ice freeze the ground. The birds cannot get at their food.

Do not forget to feed the birds during cold and frosty weather!

Question Time

1. What is the father Robin called?
2. Why is the robin called robin redbreast?
3. Which is the tamest of our garden birds?
4. Is the robin a sweet singer?
5. What is the mother Robin called?
6. What do the young birds have to learn?
7. What do robins eat?
8. What animals kill the robin?
9. What is the robin's greatest enemy?
10. What can you do for the birds during cold weather?

Look at this robin carefully. Then, write the name of each part into your book.

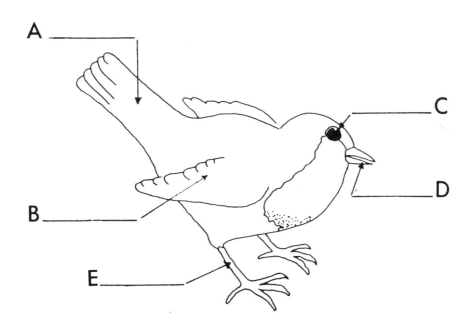

A

B

C

D

E

Phonics - long *i* with magic *e.*

pip	Say the *i* sound. It is a short sound.
pipe	Say the *i* sound It is a long sound. The magic *e* at the end turns the *i* into the name of the letter.

A. **Write the missing *i* and magic *e.*
Then *read* the word.**

K __ t __	f __ v __	f __ r __

B. **Write the missing letters.
Remember the magic e.
Then, *read* the word.**

mi _____	hi _____	di _____
ni _____	wi _____	sli _____

A. Write the missing letters. Read the sentence.

1. I l __ k __ looking at television.
2. I will r __ d __ a donkey.
3. The f __ r __ is very hot.
4. The house is a m __ l __ from the school.
5. It is t __ m __ for bed.
6. Sunday was a very f __ n __ day.
7. The apple was not r __ p __ .

B. Read each sentence carefully. Choose the correct word.

1. I cannot smoke a (pip, pipe).
2. A fish has a (fin, fine).
3. The top can (spine, spin) very well.
4. I love to (rid, ride) my bicycle.
5. I will (win, wine) the race.
6. It is very rude to (spite, spit).
7. I can (slide, slid) on the ice.
8. My Mummy and Daddy drink (win, wine).

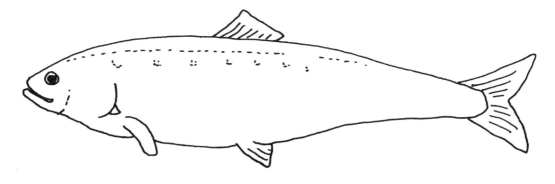

The Boy Who Cried Wolf

Once there was a boy who looked after sheep on a hill. He did not like being alone.

One day, he said to himself, "I am so bored! Just for fun I will call **Wolf! Wolf!** and everybody will come running."

So he did call **Wolf! Wolf!**. Many people came. "Ha, ha, ha," he laughed, "it was only a joke." He did this three times. Each time the people came he told them that there was no wolf.

But, one day, the wolf **did** come. "**Help, help,** the wolf is here," the boy cried. But everyone said: "We know that there is no wolf. That boy is tricking us. There is no danger. This time we will not go!"

So the people did not go and the wolf killed all the sheep.

A. Question Time.

1. What was the boy looking after?
2. Where did the boy look after the sheep?
3. What did the boy not like?
4. What did the boy call one day?
5. Why did the boy call "Wolf! Wolf!"?
6. What happened when he shouted "Wolf! Wolf!" the first time?
7. Did he call "Wolf! Wolf!" in fun often?
8. When the wolf really came what did people think?
9. What did the wolf do?
10. How do you think the boy felt?

B. Choose the correct word.

1. The boy was looking after (sheep, pigs, goats).
2. The boy was alone on (a farm, a hill, a truck).
3. The boy was (happy, sad, bored).
4. The boy cried (help!, wolf!, danger!).
5. The boy thought he was (funny, clever, stupid).
6. A wolf is (wild, tame, friendly).
7. A wolf eats (meat, vegetables, grass).
8. A wolf looks like a (dog, cat, rabbit).
9. The wolf killed (the boy, the sheep, the people).
10. The boy was (clever, funny, foolish).

Grammar

The names of places always begin with capital letters.

A.   Write these sentences correctly.

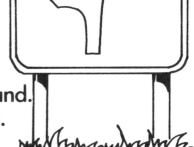

1. sheffield is a big city.
2. We live in britain.
3. I stayed in a caravan in wales.
4. glasgow is far from london.
5. bradford is next to leeds.
6. We are going on holidays to scotland.
7. Ann went to land's end in cornwall.
8. A big ship sails to america.

B.   Put *do* or *does* in the space.

1. I _____ my homework every night.
2. You _____ not know your spellings.
3. Ann _____ the shopping.
4. _____ he want to go swimming?
5. The children _____ a lot of work.
6. _____ it always rain here?
7. You _____ not use bad words.
8. The teacher _____ not slap us.

Puzzle time 2

Read the clues.
Write the answers in your book.

Clues.

1. Two fives.
2. Add three to six.
3. A half of eight.
4. Add one to ten.
5. Two fours.
6. Six plus zero.
7. Two less than three.
8. One more than eight.

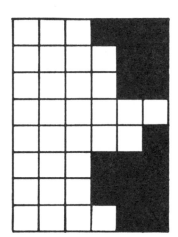

Read the clues. Write the answers.

Across
1. You kick this (8)
3. The bark on the tree is this colour (5).
4. They have leaves and branches (5)
5. Large white bird (4)
6. The little girl is doing this (8).
9. He sleeps in his pram (4).
10. Fish swim in this (4)

Down
1. They grow in beds in the park (7)
2. They fly in the sky (5)
7. The baby sleeps in this (4)
8. The grass is this colour (5)

The Cow

The cow is a big gentle animal with large brown eyes. She has a long tail which she uses to swish away flies.

Cows spend a lot of time chewing grass. Only cows that have a baby can give milk. A baby cow is called a calf.

The cow in the picture is called a Fresian. It is black and white. It gives a lot of milk. Milk is a very good food. It gives us energy. It keeps us warm and it helps us to grow. Milk can be used to make butter, cheese and yogurt.

The cow also gives us meat called beef. Beefburgers are made using beef from the cow. The cow's skin, which we call its hide, is used to make leather shoes and bags.

Question Time.

1. How does the cow use its tail?
2. What is a baby cow called?
3. What cow gives a lot of milk?
4. Why is milk a good food?
5. What can we make from milk?
6. What is cow's meat called?
7. What do we make from the cow's hide?
8. Is the cow a dangerous animal?

Put the answers into your book.

1.					s	
2.		a				
3.						r
4.	b					
5.				e		

1. Cows eat it_____
2. A baby cow is a_____
3. We put it on our bread_____
4. Cows meat is called_____
5. A cow's skin is its_____

Phonics - long *o* with magic *e*.

Read these words – h**o**p n**o**t p**o**p
Say the **o** sound. It is a short sound.

Read these words – h**o**pe n**o**te p**o**pe
Say the **o** sound. The magic **e** at the end turns the **o** into
the name of the letter.

A.   Write the missing *o* and magic *e*.
Then, *read* the words.

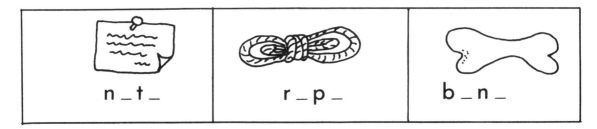

n _ t _	r _ p _	b _ n _

B.   Write the missing letters.
Remember the magic *e*.
Then, *read* the word.

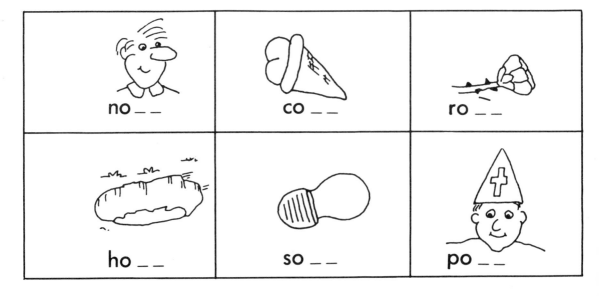

no _ _	co _ _	ro _ _
ho _ _	so _ _	po _ _

A. Write the missing letters. Read the sentence.

1. I will p _ k _ the fire.
2. I would love m _ r _ sweets.
3. I fell and my hand is s _ r _ .
4. The baby t _ r _ the book.
5. A j _ k _ makes me laugh.
6. I h _ p _ you will be better soon.
7. John has a long n _ s _ .
8. The r _ s _ is a lovely flower.

B. Read each sentence carefully. Choose the correct word.

1. The (pop, pope) lives in Rome.
2. I am (not, note) going swimming.
3. I will wash the floor with a (mope, mop).
4. I (rod, rode) a horse yesterday.
5. We (hop, hope) it will be a nice day.
6. A (cod, code) is a fish.
7. The wicked boy will (robe, rob) a shop.
8. Remember to (dot, dote) your letters.

Snow! Snow!

"Look, look,  shouted the . . . .

They put on their and boots and ran out to the

as fast as they could. "Let's make a snowman"

They rolled the snow into a big ball. They put a

smaller ball on top of the ball. They put small bits of

coal in the face for eyes. Its face was made

from a carrot. They put an old pipe in its mouth and an

old hat on its face. "Our snowman is the best one in

the world" shouted the children.

42

Question Time.

1. Who shouted "snow, snow"?
2. What did the children wear?
3. Where did the children go?
4. How did the children make the snowman's body?
5. What part of his body was the small ball of snow?
6. What were his eyes made of?
7. What did the children use to make the nose.
8. What did the snowman have in his mouth?
9. What was the snowman wearing?
10. Were the children happy with the snowman?

Choose the correct word.

1. The children saw (fire, snow, rain).
2. They put on their (slippers, wellingtons, shoes).
3. They ran out into the (street, yard, garden).
4. They wanted to make a (card, snowman, cake).
5. The children (threw, rolled, kicked) the snow.
6. The snowman had eyes of (sweets, stones, coal).
7. The snowman had a (lollipop, pipe, sweet) in his mouth.
8. The snowman had a nose made of (turnip, parsnip, carrot).
9. The snowman is (white, grey, black).
10. Most snow falls in (autumn, winter, spring).

Grammar

We always write the word I with a capital letter.

A. Write these sentences correctly.

1. Look at what i did.
2. John and i are going fishing.
3. i like drawing pictures.
4. When i am big i will be a teacher.
5. What will i buy with this money?
6. You and i can run together.
7. Barry and i lost the race.
8. . . . must have a capital letter.

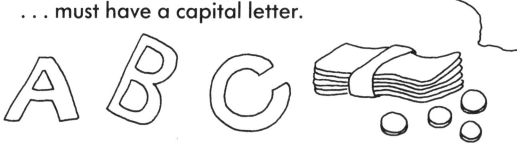

We use was when we speak about one.
We use were when we speak about more than one.

B. Put *was* or *were* in the space.

1. The book _____ lost.
2. The boys _____ very hungry.
3. The dishes _____ broken.
4. _____ you singing a song?
5. Ann _____ small but Sam and Dan _____ big.
6. They _____ very glad to be home.
7. We _____ at a concert.
8. _____ it wet yesterday?

Exercises

A. **Saturday, Monday, Friday** are all days.
Give the **group name** for each line of words below.
Choose from the **group names** in the box.

---

birds	fruit	seasons
animals	places	clothes

---

1. apple, orange, banana, grape, _____
2. spring, summer, autumn, winter, _____
3. skirt, dress, shirt, trousers, _____
4. gull, robin, chicken, goose, _____
5. London, Liverpool, Bristol, Oxford, _____
6. fox, squirrel, rabbit, mouse. _____

---

by, bye, buy.

Examples: — They walked **by** the river.
I said **bye-bye** to Daddy.
I will **buy** three oranges.

B. **Put** *by, bye,* **or** *buy* **in the space.**

1. I have to _____ a new pencil.
2. John, are you going _____ the school?
3. Peter said _____ _____ to his friend.
4. I don't have the money to _____ sweets.
5. Teacher said good _____ to us all.
6. The bus went _____ the bus stop.
7. Where can you _____ a paper?
8. _____ _____ everyone, I'm going!

The Chimpanzee

The chimpanzee is called "chimp" for short. It is the animal that looks most like man.

Chimps are friendly, playful animals. They have very strong hands and feet for swinging from branch to branch. Chimps eat a lot of fruit. They love bananas. An adult chimp can eat up to 40 bananas at one time!

A baby chimp is carried by its mother until it is 5 months old. Then, it learns how to walk. It stays close to its mother until it is 4 years old.

Chimps spend a lot of time combing each others hair using their lips, teeth and fingers. They get rid of dust and insects.

When chimps meet they often kiss, rub noses or smile to show that they are friends.

The chimp is a clever animal. It can be taught tricks and sign language.

Question Time

1. What is the short name for a chimpanzee?
2. Is the chimpanzee a dangerous animal?
3. What does the chimp have to help him swing?
4. What food do chimps eat a lot of?
5. Would an adult chimp eat many bananas?
6. At what age does a baby chimp learn to walk?
7. What do chimps use to comb each other?
8. How do chimps show that they are friends?
9. In what way is the chimp a clever animal?
10. Where would you see a chimp?

Help the baby chimp to find its mother.

Phonics - "ee".

f<u>ee</u>d   b<u>ee</u>   sh<u>ee</u>p

When two e's come together the sound they make is the name of the letter "e".

A. Put *"ee"* into each word. Read the word.

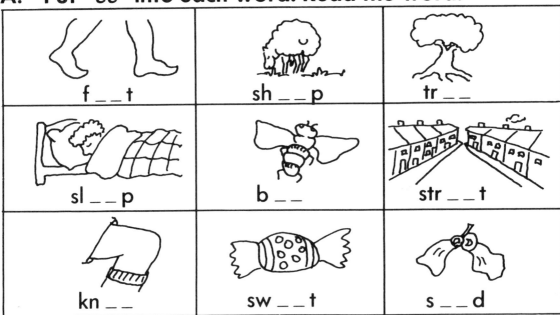

f _ _ t   sh _ _ p   tr _ _

sl _ _ p   b _ _   str _ _ t

kn _ _   sw _ _ t   s _ _ d

B. Choose the correct word from the words given above.

1. We get wool from _____ .
2. A _____ flies from flower to flower.
3. I have a _____ after my lunch.
4. I have two hands and two _____ .
5. I live on a long _____ .
6. I fell and cut my _____ .
7. You can climb a _____ .
8. I must go to _____ in bed.
9. I planted a _____ in a pot.

Phonics - "oo"

school   balloon   food

When **two o's** come together the sound they make is like a long "u".

A. Put "oo" into each word. Read the word.

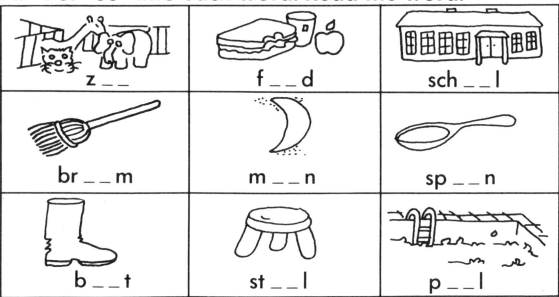

z _ _	f _ _ d	sch _ _ l
br _ _ m	m _ _ n	sp _ _ n
b _ _ t	st _ _ l	p _ _ l

B. Choose the correct words from the words given above.

1. We need _____ to grow.
2. I can see the man in the _____ .
3. I am sitting on a _____ .
4. I love to visit the _____ .
5. I work very hard in _____ .
6. The witch has a _____ .
7. I eat my porridge with a _____ .
8. I can't tie my other _____ .
9. I go swimming in the _____ .

Spring

The months of spring are February, March and April. The weather gets a little warmer and the days a little longer.

Yellow catkins make the hedges brighter. The trees now have buds from which leaves will grow.

The birds are busy building nests and laying eggs. The swallow and the cuckoo come back to Britain.

We see snowdrops and crocuses in the garden. Wild flowers like the bluebell and the primrose can also be seen.

Many lambs are born in spring. They can be seen in the fields, running and jumping near their mothers. The hare is also having fun "boxing" other hares.

Frogs lay their eggs. We call them frogspawn. They will turn into tadpoles and later frogs.

The farmer is busy sowing wheat and corn. In the garden we plant vegetables and flowers which will grow in the summer.

Question Time.

1. What are the months of spring?
2. How many months are there in spring?
3. What appears on the trees in spring?
4. What bird returns to Britain in spring?
5. What do the birds do in spring?
6. What flowers grow in the garden in spring?
7. What animal is born in spring?
8. What are frogs' eggs called?
9. What does the farmer sow in spring?
10. Name two vegetables you can plant in your garden in spring?

Spring

Trace and colour the pictures. Finish off the words.

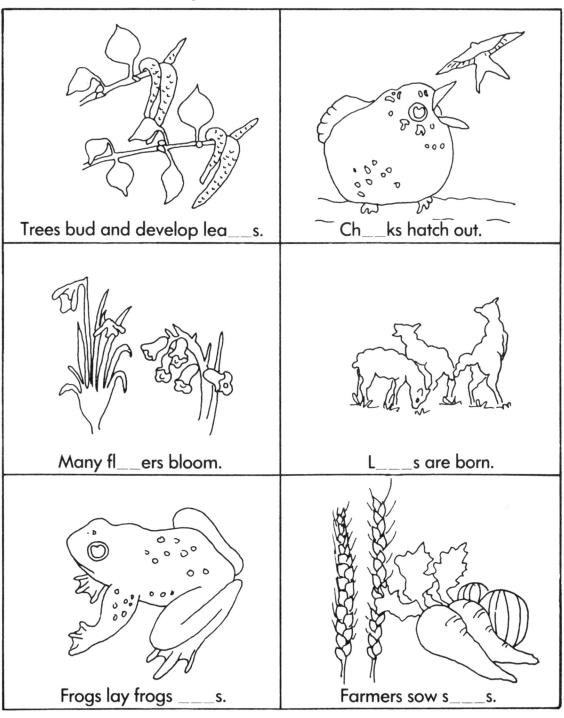

Trees bud and develop lea___s.

Ch___ks hatch out.

Many fl___ers bloom.

L____s are born.

Frogs lay frogs ____s.

Farmers sow s____s.

The Lion And The Mouse

One day a lion was asleep under a tree. A little mouse ran over his paw. The lion lifted his paw to crush the mouse. "Please, please, do not kill me," squeaked the mouse.

The lion took pity on her.

"Thank you," said the mouse, "One day I will help you."

"Ha, ha, ha," laughed the lion. "A little mouse like you, help the King of the Jungle." Some days later, the lion walked into a trap. He could not free himself. He roared and roared. Suddenly, he heard a little squeak. The mouse was beside him. She nibbled at the ropes and in no time the lion was free.

The lion thanked the mouse.

"You have saved my life," he said. The lion and the mouse became great friends.

Question Time

1. Where was the lion asleep?
2. What ran over the lion's paw?
3. What was the lion going to do?
4. What did the mouse say to the lion?
5. Did the lion believe the mouse?
6. What happened to the lion some days later?
7. What did the lion do when he could not free himself?
8. How did the mouse free the lion?
9. What did the lion say to the mouse?
10. Did the lion and the mouse become friends?

Choose the correct word.

1. The lion was (awake, asleep, eating) under a tree.
2. A (horse, rat, mouse) ran over his paw.
3. A lion is a wild (dog, monkey, cat).
4. A mouse is (smaller, bigger, fatter) than a lion.
5. The lion is the king of (the castle, the country, the jungle).
6. The lion walked into a (house, farm, trap).
7. The mouse (roared, squeaked, barked).
8. The mouse (nibbled, tore, broke) the rope.
9. The lion (thanked, killed, ate) the mouse.
10. The lion and the mouse became (enemies, friends, brothers).

Grammar

We always write the days and months with a capital letter.

A.   Write the following sentences correctly.

1. On monday we start school.
2. january is the first month of the year.
3. We do not go to school in august.
4. It is my birthday on sunday.
5. may is the first month of summer.
6. I go swimming every wednesday.
7. Mummy went to the doctor on tuesday.
8. Christmas comes in december.

B.   Put _has_ or _have_ in the space.

1. Peter _____ a new coat on to-day.
2. I _____ a present for you.
3. John and Alan _____ a football.
4. What _____ the children got?
5. Many people _____ no food.
6. _____ the bus passed yet?
7. Ann _____ a big balloon.
8. I _____ no pen to write with.

Exercises

A. Look at the words on each line. One **word** is an odd-man-out. It **does not belong** to the same family as the others. **Write it in your book.**

1. teacher, Ann, nurse, milk-man, doctor   _____
2. yellow, blue, green, sky, white   _____
3. apple, pear, turnip, peach, plum   _____
4. jumper, skirt, dress, leg, hat   _____
5. piano, violin, triangle, wood, drum   _____
6. plate, table, cup, saucer, jug   _____
7. elephant, tiger, giraffe, goose, crocodile _____
8. rose, daffodil, carrot, snowdrop   _____

---

where   were

Example: — We **were** at the circus.
         Where is the film on?
         Were you good yesterday?
         I know **where** I'm going.

B. **Put _where_ or _were_ in the space.**

1. John knows _____ Peter lives.
2. Who _____ you playing with?
3. We _____ told to be in early.
4. _____ is the nearest shop?
5. We _____ not at school on Saturday.
6. _____ is the teacher living?
7. You and I _____ very good swimmers.
8. I can't see _____ I put my bag.

The Seagull

This sea-gull is called a herring gull. He is a large bird with grey and white feathers. His feet are webbed to help him swim.

Seagulls can follow ships across the sea for hours. They are watching all the time for bits of food. They have very sharp eyes.

Gulls build their nests in spring on the ledges of the cliffs. The nests are made of roots, grass and dry seaweed.

When the weather at sea is bad the gulls often come inland. We hear their sharp cries. They are looking for food.

Question Time

1. Where do seagulls live?
2. What colours are the herring gulls feathers?
3. Why do gulls have webbed feet?
4. Why do gulls follow ships?
5. Where do gulls build their nests?
6. What are gulls' nests made of?
7. When do gulls sometimes come inland?
8. Why do gulls come inland?
9. Did you ever see a sea-gull?
10. Where did you see it?

Can you finish the words in the puzzle?

1.			n			
2.		l				
3.	w					
4.	n					
5.		h				

1. Birds use them to fly.
2. Where gulls build their nests.
3. Gulls' feet are . . . . . .
4. Gulls build their . . . . . . in spring.
5. The cry of the gull is . . . .

Phonics - *bl, cl, fl, gl, pl, sl.*

A. Look at each picture. Circle the sound at the beginning of each word.

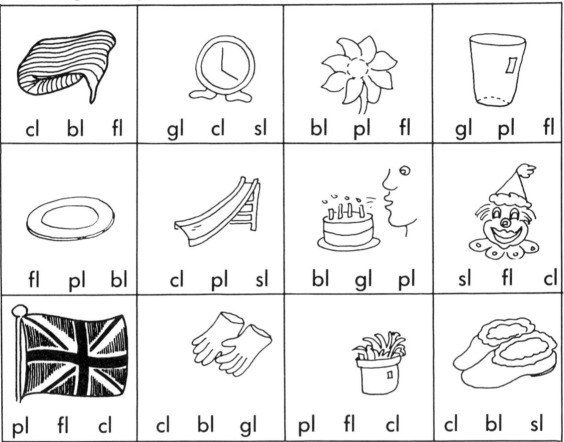

cl bl fl	gl cl sl	bl pl fl	gl pl fl
fl pl bl	cl pl sl	bl gl pl	sl fl cl
pl fl cl	cl bl gl	pl fl cl	cl bl sl

Read each sentence

B. Write the missing vowel in the word.

1. I can cl _ p my hands.
2. I was very gl _ d to see the sun.
3. The bath pl _ g is missing.
4. Mummy will eat a pl_m.
5. Do not sl_p on the ice.

6. The fl_g is red, white and blue.
7. Some children live in a fl _ t.
8. The cl _ ck shows the time.
9. There are many sl _ gs in the garden.
10. I put a cl _ p in my hair.

A. Put bl, cl, fl, gl, pl, or sl in the blank space. Read the word.

_ _ ood	_ _ oud	_ _ y
_ _ ider	_ _ ate	_ _ eep
_ _ aws	_ _ ames	_ _ ay

B. Choose the correct word from the words given above.

1. I saw _____ when I cut my finger.
2. A lion has sharp _____ .
3. A _____ flies in the air.
4. A fire has _____ .
5. I _____ with my friends.
6. I can see a _____ in the sky.
7. The _____ is going up the wall.
8. I need a _____ for my cake.
9. I go to _____ at night.

Exercises

A. Match each person to their job.

butcher	policeman	chemist	dentist
doctor	postman	farmer	teacher

1. We get meat in the _____ shop.
2. The _____ grows wheat and barley.
3. We get medicine from the _____ .
4. We go to the _____ when we are sick.
5. If I get lost I will talk to a _____ .
6. The _____ looks after my teeth.
7. Here comes the _____ with letters.
8. The _____ helps me to learn.

---

their   there

Example: — They are in **their** house.
We are going over **there**.
Their Mummy is sick.
There is the dog.

B. Put _their_ or _there_ in the space.

1. They are going on _____ holidays.
2. Look at what I found _____ .
3. _____ doctor is very kind.
4. They put on _____ coats.
5. _____ cat had kittens.
6. What's going on in _____ ?
7. Why is _____ television not working?
8. _____ is a dead mouse in the house.

Puzzle time 3

Read the clues. Write the answers.

Across
1. You can push somebody on this (5)
3. You can dig the sand with this (5)
4. You go here to learn (6)
5. You throw the ball into this (3)
8. You can kick this (4)
10. It is green. You can play ball on it (5)

Down
2. You eat this from a cone (3, 5)
3. The children play on this (5)
4. You can make castles with this (4, 3)
6. She helps you learn (7)
7. The sky is this colour (4)
9. They have leaves and branches (5)

Choose a word from the box that rhymes with one below. Write it.

bad	dig	hug
mud	red	got
tin	but	

1. **mad** goes with . . . .
3. **pig** goes with . . . .
5. **nut** goes with . . . .
7. **not** goes with . . . .
2. **rug** goes with . . . .
4. **bed** goes with . . . .
6. **pin** goes with . . . .
8. **bud** goes with . . . .

The Real Princess

Once upon a time, there lived a prince, who wished to marry a princess, but, she had to be a **real** princess. He looked far and wide but was not able to find one.

One wet, windy evening there came a knock on the door of the palace. Outside stood a princess who was very, very wet. She said that she was a **real** princess.

"We shall see about that!" thought the queen. The queen made up a bed for the princess to sleep in. On the bed she put three little peas. On top of the peas she put twenty mattresses.

The next morning the queen asked the princess how she had slept.

"Oh, very badly indeed! I do not know what was in my bed but I had something hard under me and now I am black and blue all over".

"This is a **real** princess," said the queen because she felt the peas under all the mattresses. So the prince and the **real** princess married.

Question Time.

1. Who did the prince want to marry?
2. What kind of evening was it when the princess came to the palace?
3. What did the princess look like when she knocked on the door?
4. What did the queen put in the princess's bed?
5. What did the queen ask the princess when she got up?
6. Did the princess sleep well?
7. Why did the princess not sleep well?
8. Did the prince and the princess marry?

Choose the correct word.

1. The prince wanted to marry a (princess, a queen, a maid).
2. It was a (wet, dry, snowy) evening.
3. The prince lived in a (stable, school, palace).
4. The princess looked (ugly, beautiful, wet) when she knocked at the door.
5. The queen made up a (lunch, dress, bed) for the princess.
6. The queen put (beans, peas, stones) on the bed.
7. The queen put (two, twenty, twenty-two) mattresses on top of the peas.
8. The princess slept (well, badly, perfectly).

Sheep

Sheep are shy animals that live in **flocks.** They copy one another. Usually they all eat together and rest together.

There are many different breeds of sheep. Some sheep live on hill farms. The farmer on a hill farm uses a sheepdog to gather his flock of sheep and to move them from one place to another.

The mother sheep is called a **ewe.** The father sheep is a **ram.** Baby sheep, which are born in the spring, are called **lambs.** When lambs are about three weeks old they start to play together. They race and have mock fights.

As the weather gets warmer the farmer shears the sheeps' wool. Many of our clothes such as coats, scarves and gloves are made from wool. Wool keeps us warm.

A sheep's skin can be used to make rugs, gloves and slippers.

Question Time.

1. Are sheep friendly animals?
2. What do we call a group of sheep?
3. What do sheep do together?
4. What job does a sheepdog do?
5. What is a mother sheep called?
6. What is a father sheep called?
7. When are lambs born?
8. What do young lambs do?
9. When does the farmer shear his sheep?
10. Name three items that are made of wool.

Write out the sentence. Put *true* or *false* after it.

1. Sheep are dangerous animals. _____
2. Sheep live in herds. _____
3. A mother sheep is a ewe. _____
4. A father sheep is a bull. _____
5. Lambs are born in autumn. _____
6. Sheep dogs look after cows. _____
7. We get wool from sheep. _____
8. We eat sheeps' meat. _____
9. A sheep has a coat of hair. _____
10. Wool keeps us cold. _____

Phonics - *ea, ai, oa.*

m e a t

When two vowels go out walking the first one does the talking and it takes the name of the letter.

So in meat e does the talking and it has a long e sound.

A. Put "ea" into the following words.

s _ _	m _ _ t	s _ _ l
l _ _ ves	p _ _ s	t _ _ m

B. Choose the correct word from the words given above.

1. The _____ are falling from the trees.
2. The _____ is swimming in the sea.
3. The _____ is very rough today.
4. The cow gives us _____ .
5. _____ grow in a pod.
6. I play on a football _____ .

r a i n   "ai" "oa"

coat

When 2 vowels go out walking the first one does the talking and it takes the name of the letter.

In rain, a does the talking and it has a long sound.

In coat, o does the talking and it has a long o sound.

A. Put "ai" or "oa" into the following words.

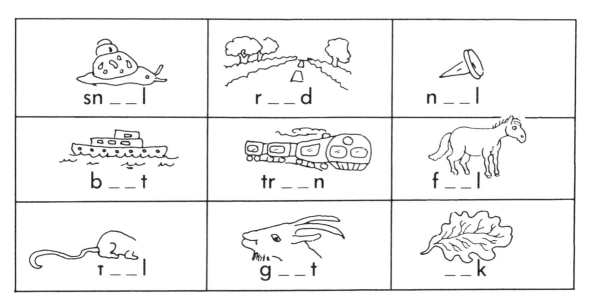

sn _ _ l	r _ _ d	n _ _ l
b _ _ t	tr _ _ n	f _ _ l
r _ _ l	g _ _ t	_ _ k

B. Choose the correct word from the words given above.

1. I hit the _____ with my hammer.
2. The car is going down the _____ .
3. The _____ has a shell on its back.
4. A baby horse is called a _____ .
5. The dog is wagging his _____ .
6. I see a _____ on the pond.
7. The _____ is in the station.
8. A _____ has babies called kids.
9. An acorn is the fruit of an _____ .

Exercises

A. Put one of the following words in each space.

---

zoo   hive   school   garage

cinema   barracks   tank   wardrobe

---

1. Soldiers live in a _____ .
2. Bees live in a _____ .
3. Cars are kept in a _____ .
4. Films are shown in a _____ .
5. Pupils can be seen in a _____ .
6. Water is kept in a _____ .
7. Wild animals can be seen in a _____ .
8. We hang our clothes in a _____ .

---

no   know.
Examples: — Do you **know** my name?
               Sorry, I don't **know** it.
               The children have **no** food.
               No, it is not cold today.

B. Put _no_ or _know_ in the space.

1. I _____ all my tables.
2. I said _____ to the teacher.
3. Do you _____ how to bake?
4. Peter has _____ towel to dry himself.
5. Alan doesn't _____ his colours.
6. Ann had _____ food for her lunch.
7. _____ I will not go to bed!
8. I have _____ money to buy a ball.

Grammar

We use *capital letters* **for the following: —**

a)   at the start of all sentences
b)   for the names of people
c)   for the names of places
d)   for the word I
e)   for the names of the days and months

REMEMBER!

We put a *full stop* **at the end of a sentence.**

Write the following sentences correctly.

1. i live in hull
2. peter and mary go swimming on tuesday
3. you and i are driving to nottingham
4. emma has a granny in belfast
5. next september ann will be eight
6. i am going to work on monday and friday
7. we have no school on sunday
8. look at john and sharon
9. i lost my hat on the bus to cork
10. i am going to spain in october

The Circus Comes To Town

Peter and Ann were in [houses] . The circus parade

came up [street] . The [clowns] came first.

They wore baggy [pants] and tall red [hats] .

Everybody laughed at the [clowns] . Then came a big

[circus truck] . The [lions] were in the [circus truck]

Ann fed the [monkey] . The [elephant] waved its long

[trunk] . "Please [Mother] and [Father] , may we go to the

[tent] ?" said Peter and Ann.

Question Time

1. Who was in town?
2. What came up the street?
3. What came first in the parade?
4. What did the clowns wear?
5. Who were people laughing at?
6. What was in the van?
7. Who fed the monkey?
8. What did the elephant wave?
9. Where did Ann and Peter want to go?
10. Have you been to the circus?

Choose the correct word.

1. Peter and Ann were in (school, church, town).
2. The (band, car, circus) came up the street.
3. The (elephant, lions, clown) came first.
4. The clowns wore (short, baggy, long) trousers.
5. Everybody (cried, laughed, shouted) at the clowns.
6. There were (elephants, monkeys, lions) in the van.
7. Ann fed a (dog, fish, monkey).
8. A monkey is (a bird, a fish, an animal).
9. An (elephant, otter, ostrich) has a trunk.
10. The circus makes me (happy, sad, angry).

Grammar

Some sentences ask questions.
These words ask a question.

where? who? why?
what? when? how?

A question must have a question mark at the end.

A. Copy out the sentences.
Put in a _question mark_ or a _full stop_.

1. Where is your sister today
2. I love apples and oranges
3. How is your granny who is sick
4. We play football on Saturday
5. Who ate up all my dinner
6. Why is Daddy still in bed
7. John looks at too much television
8. What is Ann eating

B. Put _did_ or _done_ in the spaces.

1. I _____ my reading.
2. Who _____ all the washing-up?
3. I have _____ all the drawing.
4. When the work was _____ we went to bed.
5. Ann _____ a lot of housework.
6. We have _____ the gardening.
7. We _____ the writing on page two.
8. She _____ what the others had _____

Exercises

A. **Write the** opposites **in the space.**
Choose from the words given below.

sweet	bright	slow	empty
false	fresh	heavy	noisy

1. An orange can be bitter or _____ .
2. A bag can be light or _____ .
3. A train can be fast or _____ .
4. A bottle can be full or _____ .
5. A loaf of bread can be stale or _____ .
6. Children can be quiet or _____ .
7. The day can be dull or _____ .
8. Something we write can be true or _____ .

wood   would.

Examples: — We put some **wood** on the fire.
        I **would** like a glass of milk.

B.   **Put** _wood_ **or** _would_ **in the space.**

1. Where _____ you like to go on holiday?
2. The table is made of _____ .
3. The _____ is very thick.
4. John _____ not sing at school.
5. We get a lot of _____ from an oak tree.
6. Who _____ like some cake?
7. The cabin is built from _____ .
8. It _____ rain when I have to go out!

The Ladybird

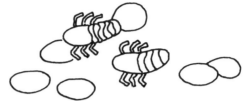

This ladybird has eggs. She lays them on a plant covered in greenfly.

The eggs hatch out. Out creep dark grubs. Each one has 6 legs. They eat the greenfly.

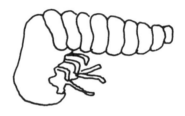

The grubs eat and eat until their skins burst. They creep out of the old skins.

The grubs now have grey blue skin. They eat again until full. They hang upside down. Their skins burst. Each grub has become a chrysalis.

One week later a yellow ladybird creeps out. After a while it gets its red colour and seven black spots.

The ladybird flies away to look for food because it could not eat as a chrysalis.

A frog catches the ladybird. it squirts a yellow liquid at the frog. Oh! It's horrible! The frog drops the ladybird.

It is autumn. The ladybird finds a crack in the bark of an apple tree. It creeps inside with another ladybird and goes to sleep.

Question Time.

1. Where does the ladybird lay her eggs?
2. What comes out of the eggs?
3. What do grubs eat?
4. What does a grub become?
5. How long does a chrysalis last?
6. How many spots has a ladybird?
7. Why does the new ladybird want food?
8. What does the ladybird do if it is in danger?
9. What does the ladybird do in autumn?

Take the ladybird to the cabbage leaf.

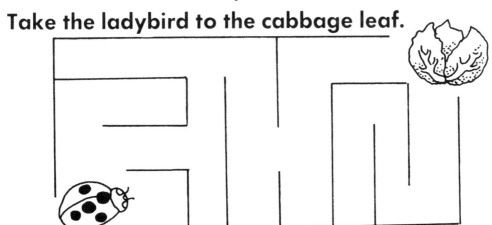

Phonics - *br, cr, dr, fr, gr, pr, tr.*

Look at each picture.

A. **Write out which is the sound at the beginning of each word.**

br dr gr	pr cr tr	br gr dr
fr br dr	pr gr dr	br cr pr
tr fr pr	dr br gr	gr pr cr
pr br gr	fr dr pr	br tr pr

B. **Put br, cr, dr, fr, gr, pr, or tr, in the blank space.**

1. I have a pretty ____ ess.
2. The ____ ass is green.
3. The farmer drives a ____ actor.
4. A ____ og has tadpoles.
5. I ____ ush my hair everyday.

6. I got a ____ esent on my birthday.
7. Never smile at a ____ ocodile.
8. A ____ iangle has three sides.
9. ____ ead is made from flour.
10. There are green ____ apes and black ____ apes.

A. Put tr, cr, dr, fr, gr, pr **or** tr **in the space.**

____ idge	____ ane	____ iend
____ ay	____ icks	____ awer
____ umpet	____ avy	____ ousers

B. Choose the correct word from the words given above.

1. The wall is made of _____ .
2. A _____ lifts heavy things.
3. A _____ goes over the river.
4. My _____ is full of socks.
5. John is my best _____ .
6. I like _____ on my dinner.
7. Some people _____ to God.
8. I can play the _____ .
9. I wear blue _____ .

77

Summer

The months of summer are May, June and July. In summer the days are much warmer and sunnier.

The bees are busy collecting pollen from the flowers. They "comb" the pollen from their hair into "baskets" on their hind legs.

In the air we smell the blossom of the hawthorn. The butterfly enjoys the sunshine and the honey of the wildflowers, such as, the buttercup and the daisy.

The frogspawn have turned into tadpoles, soon they will grow legs. Then, their tails will drop off and they will be frogs.

The woods are filled with the song of the cuckoo, the blackbird, the thrush and other birds.

In the garden we find tulips, lilies and roses. The sweetest smelling summer flower is the rose.

On the farm the farmer is cutting the hay. Among the straw, red poppies grow.

Question Time

1. What are the months of summer?
2. How many months are there in summer?
3. How does summer weather differ from winter weather?
4. What do bees collect from the flowers?
5. What do butterflies enjoy?
6. What happens to frogspawn?
7. What garden flowers grow in summer?
8. Name one job that the farmer does in summer?
9. What kind of clothes do you wear in summer?
10. Why do you like summer?

Trace and colour the pictures. Finish off the words.

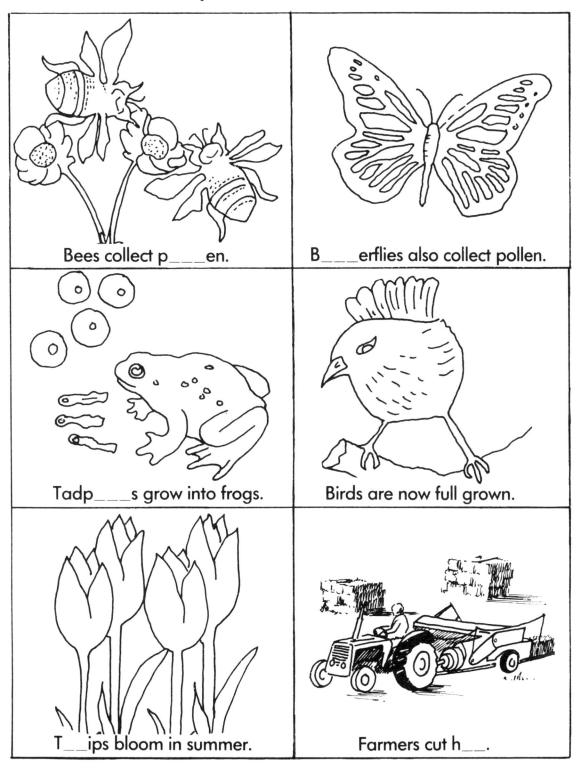

Bees collect p____en.

B____erflies also collect pollen.

Tadp____s grow into frogs.

Birds are now full grown.

T__ips bloom in summer.

Farmers cut h__.

The Goose That Laid The Golden Eggs

Once an old man and an old woman had a goose. It was a very special goose. Every day it laid a golden egg.

The old man and woman sold the eggs for lots of money. But, the more money they had, the more they wanted.

They said, "If our goose lays golden eggs she must be made of gold. Let us cut her open and get out all the gold at once. Then we will have more money."

They killed the goose but found no gold. When they cut their goose open they saw that she was just like any other goose.

After that there were no more golden eggs so they did not get any more money.

In the end they had nothing.

Question Time

1. Who had a goose?
2. Why was the goose special?
3. How often did it lay an egg?
4. What did the old man and woman do with the eggs?
5. What did they think the goose must be made of?
6. Why did they kill the goose?
7. What did they find when they cut the goose open?
8. Why was there no more money?
9. Were the couple richer or poorer after they killed the goose?
10. What kind of people would you think the old couple were?

Choose the correct word.

1. The man and woman were (young, middle-aged, old).
2. The couple had a (duck, swan, goose).
3. A goose is a (fish, bird, insect).
4. A goose has (two, four, six) legs.
5. A goose has a coat of (scales, fur, feathers).
6. The eggs were made of (silver, gold, metal).
7. The eggs were sold for (food, money, clothes).
8. Gold is worth (little, much, nothing).
9. The couple were (kind, selfish, greedy).
10. The couple had (more, less, nothing) when they killed the goose.

Grammar

A _naming_ word is a person, place, or thing. _Naming_ words are called _nouns_.

A. Write out these sentences. Put a circle around the _naming_ words.

1. Cows eat grass.
2. The boy kicked the ball.
3. The children ate sweets.
4. Hens lay eggs.
5. The table is long.
6. The man lit his pipe.
7. The teacher wrote a letter.
8. The indian lives in a wigwam.

B. Finish each sentence using a _naming_ word from the box.

axe	key	knife	saw
pen	hammer	kettle	soap

1. I cut through the wood with a _____ .
2. I lock the door with a _____ .
3. I write the letter with a _____ .
4. I hit the nail with a _____ .
5. I chop down the tree with an _____ .
6. I boil the water in a _____ .
7. I cut the cake with a _____ .
8. I wash my hands with _____ .

Puzzle time 4

A. Read the clues. Write the answers.

Across
1. You can carry water in this (6)
6. Baby cows (6)
7. You get wool from these (5)
8. Where does milk come from   (3)
9. Hens lay these (4)
11. Meow! I like milk (3)

Down
1. You sweep with this (5)
2. The farmer drives this (7)
3. What is in the churns? (4)
4. One goose, two ___ (5)
5. We get eggs from them (4)
10. This is a Billy _____ (4)

B. Read the clues. Write the answers.

1. The day after Tuesday.
    _____

2. The last day of the week.
    _____

3. The first day of the week.
    _____

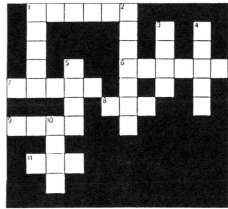

4. The day between Wednesday and Friday.
    _____

5. The day before Saturday.
    _____

6. The third day of the week.
    _____

7. The day between Sunday and Tuesday.
    _____

Fish

All fish live in water. Some live in salt water – that is sea water. Other fish live in fresh water.

A fish is a very good swimmer. It uses its tail to move along through the water.

A fish has fins on each side of its body. It uses its fins to balance itself.

A fish's body is covered with scales. On the sides of its head it has gills. Gills are openings that help the fish to breathe.

**Look at the different parts of the fish.
Finish the words.**

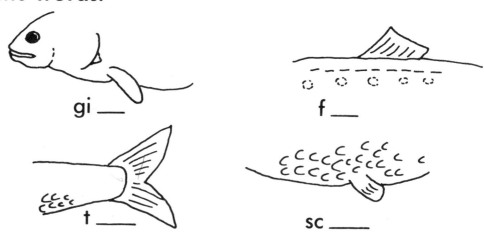

gi ___

f ___

t ___

sc ___

Question Time
1. How does a fish use its tail?
2. How do a fish's fins help it?
3. What do we call the covering on a fish's body?
4. What does a fish breathe through?
5. What must all fish live in?
6. Name 3 fish you know.

Shellfish

When you find an empty shell the animal that lived inside it is dead. The animal makes the shell from a special liquid that comes from its body.

The shell grows as the animal inside it grows. Some people love the meat of shellfish such as mussels, lobster and crab.

A crab has ten legs. The two front legs have pincers on them. A crab will pinch you if you go too close. A crab walks sideways.

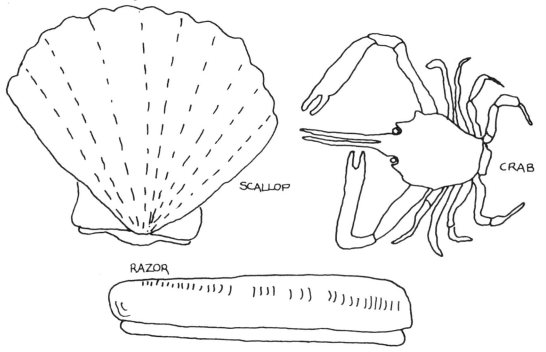

SCALLOP

CRAB

RAZOR

Find the words you need above.

1. Shells are made from a special _____
2. A crab has _____ legs.
3. A crab has _____ pincers.
4. Crabs walk _____

Phonics — *sh, ch, th*

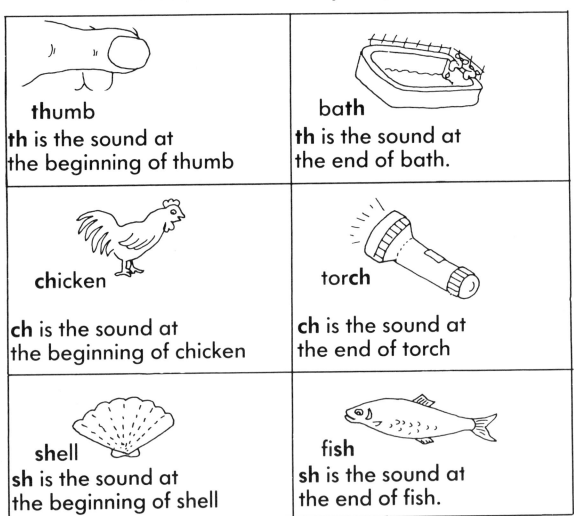

thumb

th is the sound at the beginning of thumb

bath

th is the sound at the end of bath.

chicken

ch is the sound at the beginning of chicken

tor**ch**

ch is the sound at the end of torch

shell

sh is the sound at the beginning of shell

fi**sh**

sh is the sound at the end of fish.

A.   Look at each picture. Which is the sound at the beginning of each word.

th ch sh	th ch sh	sh th ch
ch th sh	sh th ch	sh ch th

ch th sh	sh ch th	th sh ch
sh ch th	sh ch th	th sh ch

A.   Write the missing letters. Read the sentence.

1. I cut my _ _ umb.
2. We will find a _ _ ell at the beach.
3. I wear _ _ oes on my feet.
4. I visit the _ _ urch every Sunday.
5. I dig the garden with a _ _ ovel.
6. A rose has many _ _ orns.

B.   Write the missing letters.

bea _ _	di _ _	ba _ _
spla _ _	tor _ _	coa _ _

C.   Choose the correct word from the words given above.

1.   I play with the sand on the _____ .
2.   I eat my cereal in a _____ .
3.   I take a _____ every Saturday night.
4.   I need a _____ because it is dark.
5.   We go to the seaside in a _____ .
6.   The rain made a big _____ .

Who Can Jump Highest?

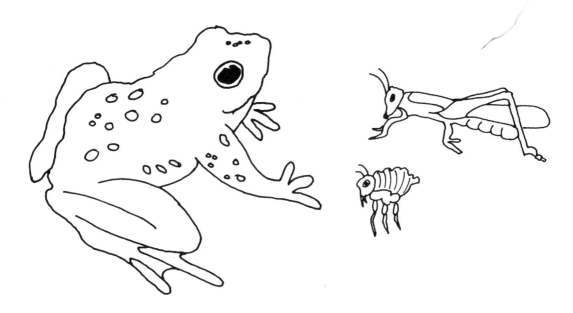

The flea, the grasshopper and the frog wanted to find out which one of them could jump the highest. They invited everybody to come and see the competition.

"I will give my daughter to the one who jumps the highest," said the king.

The flea jumped first. He jumped so high that no one could see what had become of him. Some people said that he had not jumped at all.

Next came the grasshopper who only jumped half as high, but, jumped right into the king's face. The king was very angry and thought that the grasshopper was very rude.

The frog was the last to jump. He stood so still that people thought he wasn't going to jump at all. Suddenly, the frog made a sidelong jump, right into the lap of the princess who was sitting nearby.

"There is nothing higher than my daughter," said the king. "So you frog, shall have her as your wife."

Question Time

1. Name the creatures that were jumping.
2. Who was invited to the competition?
3. What was the winner's prize?
4. Who jumped first?
5. Why did some people say that the flea hadn't jumped at all?
6. How high did the grasshopper jump?
7. Why was the king angry?
8. Why did people think that the frog wasn't going to jump at all?
9. Where did the frog jump to?
10. Who married the princess?

Choose the correct word.

1. There were (two, three, thirteen) creatures in the competition.
2. The prize was (money, a holiday, the princess).
3. The flea jumped (last, second, first).
4. The grasshopper jumped (higher than, lower than, the same as) the flea.
5. The king thought the grasshopper was (polite, cheeky, rude).
6. The frog was (noisy, still, jumpy).
7. People (love, like, hate) fleas.
8. The frog jumped (up, down, sideways).
9. The (grasshopper, flea, frog) really jumped the highest.
10. The frog was (silly, clever, stupid).

Grammar

Walk, shout, climb, grunt, fall, run, win — **these are all DOING WORDS.**

DOING WORDS are called **VERBS**.

A.   Write out these sentences. Put a circle around the *doing words.*

1.   The boy ran very fast.
2.   Pat fell off the wall.
3.   The sun shone brightly.
4.   The teacher spoke to the class.
5.   John shouted at the dog.
6.   I ran well in the race.
7.   I walked to the shop and I bought sweets.
8.   I read the book and then I lost it.

B.   Finish each sentence using a *doing word* **from the box.**

won	shouted	fell	walked
bought	spoke	barked	quacked

1.   The ducks _____ all day long.
2.   I _____ a medal at the sports.
3.   I _____ at the dog to sit.
4.   I _____ to school in the rain.
5.   Humpty Dumpty _____ off the wall.
6.   The dog _____ at the cat.
7.   I _____ an ice-cream to eat.
8.   I _____ to the dentist about my teeth.

Exercises

A. Write the words in Column A. Then, add on a word from column B to make a new word.

Column A	Column B	Column A	Column B
1. home	hole	7. pig	house
2. shoe	berry	8. farm	place
3. key	hog	9. black	ball
4. black	work	10. fire	man
5. hedge	chair	11. foot	board
6. arm	lace	12. milk	sty

Example   1.   homework

write   right

Examples: — Peter can **write** well.
I broke my **right** hand.
I **write** with a pencil.
It is **right** to tell the truth.

B. Put *write* **or** *right* **in the space.**

1. Do I turn _____ or left here?
2. Where can I _____ to you?
3. The shop is _____ in the middle of the town.
4. I _____ with my left hand.
5. It is not _____ to shout in class.
6. Will you _____ the date please?
7. Turn _____ at the church.
8. I will _____ a letter to Santa.

The Giant Panda

The giant panda lives in China. It has a tubby body, round face, small ears and a black patch around each eye. Its coat is thick and waterproof.

The panda is an excellent climber. Its strong colours help to hide it.

The panda has huge teeth and very strong jaws to eat bamboo which is very tough. It has to eat huge amounts of bamboo. It spends 14 hours a day eating. The rest of the time is spent sleeping. It has no special sleeping place.

The panda cub is tiny. It leaves its mother when it is one and a half years old to live alone.

The panda is now very rare. It is protected in China because there are so few left.

Question Time

1. Describe the panda's face.
2. How do the panda's colours help it?
3. What do pandas eat?
4. Do pandas eat much?
5. Do pandas have a special sleeping place?
6. What is a baby panda called?
7. How long does the cub spend with its mother?
8. Why do we say the panda is a rare animal?
9. In which country is the panda protected?

Write out the sentence. Put true or false after it.

1. The giant panda lives in China.＿＿＿＿＿＿＿
2. The giant panda is thin.＿＿＿＿＿＿＿＿＿
3. The giant panda is a poor climber.＿＿＿＿＿
4. The giant panda eats a lot of bamboo.＿＿＿＿
5. The giant panda spends little time eating.＿＿＿
6. Giant panda cubs are tiny.＿＿＿＿＿＿＿＿
7. The giant panda can be found everywhere.＿＿＿
8. There are many pandas in Britain. ＿＿＿＿＿

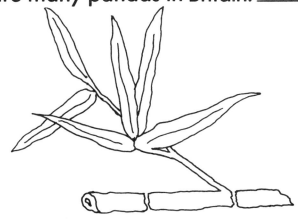

Phonics - long *a, e, i, o, u,* with magic *e.*

A. Write the missing letters.
Remember the magic e.
Then, read the word.

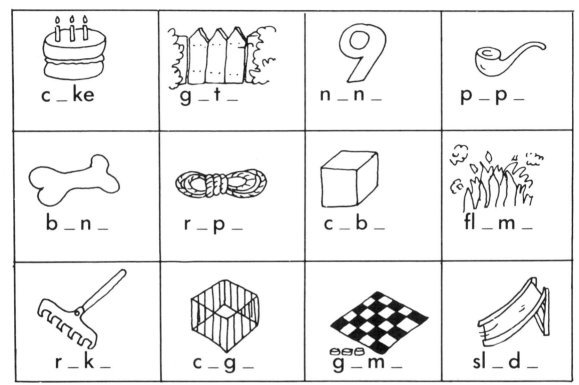

c _ ke	g _ t _	n _ n _	p _ p _
b _ n _	r _ p _	c _ b _	fl _ m _
r _ k _	c _ g _	g _ m _	sl _ d _

B. Read each sentence carefully.
Write the missing vowel and magic e..

1. The tree was knocked down in the g _ l _ .
2. I would love a b_t_ of that bar of chocolate!
3. We can h _ d _ under the stairs.
4. The t _ d _ is in because the water is high.
5. Can I tell you a j _ k _ ?
6. It is very r _ d _ to spit.
7. I w _ k _ up at 6 o'clock.
8. I would like an ice-cream c _ n _ .

94

A. Look at each picture.
Write out the word.
Every word has a magic e.

B. Read each sentence carefully.
Choose the correct word.

1. I ate a (tube, tub) of Smarties.
2. A kangaroo can (hope, hop) around.
3. I am (note, not) a good singer.
4. This apple is not very (rip, ripe).
5. The (tap, tape) is still running.
6. I broke a (pan, pane) of glass.
7. I cannot (rid, ride) your bicycle.
8. He fell and (cute, cut) his knee.
9. I (mad, made) a very big cake.
10. I will (fill, file) the bucket up.

Exercise

A. Finish each of the following sentences.

1. If I had a sweet, I would_____ .
2. If I lost my bag, I would_____ .
3. If I hit my friend_____ .
4. If it snows,_____ .
5. When I am tired, I_____ .
6. When I am hungry,_____ .
7. When I am in school,_____ .
8. When I am sad,_____ .
9. It is very hot, because_____ .
10. I ate very little, because_____ .
11. Mummy made a cake, because_____ .
12. I am happy, because_____ .

B. Put one of the following words in each space.

to, two, too, by, buy, bye, write, right, their, there, no, know.

1. I _____ a boy called Peter.
2. I _____ with my right hand.
3. It is _____ o'clock now.
4. I will _____ a new coat.
5. I can see _____ aunt coming.
6. There is _____ school on Wednesday.
7. I will run _____ the church.
8. John can swim and Paul can _____ .
9. I go home _____ the new cinema.
10. Mary said good _____ to Ann.
11. Look at that dog over _____ .
12. We drive on the _____ .